Top Of The World

Words by John Bettis. Music by Richard Carpenter.

THE COMPLETE PIANO PLAYER
CARPENTERS

Arranged by Kenneth Baker

Wise Publications
London / New York / Paris / Sydney / Copenhagen / Madrid

Exclusive Distributors:
Music Sales Limited
8/9 Frith Street,
London W1V 5TZ,
England.
Music Sales Pty Limited
120 Rothschild Avenue,
Rosebery, NSW 2018,
Australia.

This book © Copyright 1995 by Wise Publications
Order No. AM928422
ISBN 0-7119-4929-8

Book design by Studio Twenty, London
Compiled by Peter Evans
Music arranged by Kenneth Baker
Music processed by MSS Studios

Photograph courtesy of:
Redferns

Your Guarantee of Quality
As publishers, we strive to produce every book to the
highest commercial standards.
The music has been freshly engraved and the book has been
carefully designed to minimise awkward page turns and to
make playing from it a real pleasure.
Particular care has been given to specifying acid-free,
neutral-sized paper made from pulps which have not been elemental chlorine bleached.
This pulp is from farmed sustainable forests and was produced with
special regard for the environment.
Throughout, the printing and binding have been planned to ensure a sturdy,
attractive publication which should give years of enjoyment.
If your copy fails to meet our high standards, please
inform us and we will gladly replace it.

Music Sales' complete catalogue describes thousands of titles and is
available in full colour sections by subject, direct from Music Sales Limited.
Please state your areas of interest and send a cheque/postal order for £1.50 for postage to:
Music Sales Limited, Newmarket Road, Bury St. Edmunds,
Suffolk IP33 3YB.

Printed in the United Kingdom by
Halstan & Co Limited, Amersham, Buckinghamshire.

CHORUS

5

I Won't Last A Day Without You

Words by Paul Williams. Music by Roger Nichols.

Jambalaya (On The Bayou)

Words & Music by Hank Williams.

CHORUS

fun on the bay - ou._____ Jam - ba - la - ya, and a craw - fish

pie, and fil - let gum - bo._____ 'Cause to - night I'm gon - na

see my ma cher a - mi - o._____ Pick gui - tar, fill fruit

jar, and be gay - o._____ Son of a gun, we'll have big

fun on the bay - ou._____ 2. Thi - bo

We've Only Just Begun

Words by Paul Williams. Music by Roger Nichols.

Mr. Guder

Words by John Bettis. Music by Richard Carpenter.

13

Solitaire

Words & Music by Philip Cody & Neil Sedaka.

Goodbye To Love

Words by John Bettis. Music by Richard Carpenter.

Let Me Be The One

Words by Paul Williams. Music by Roger Nichols.

19

An Old Fashioned Love Song

Words & Music by Paul Williams.

ne - ver go.

You'll swear you've heard it be - fore,___ as it

slow - ly ram - bles on and on.___ No need in

bring - ing 'em back,___ 'cause they've ne - ver real - ly gone.

CHORUS

Just an old___ fash - ioned love song,___

One Love

Words by John Bettis. Music by Richard Carpenter.

Superstar

Words & Music by Leon Russell & Bonnie Bramlett.

CHORUS

real - ly here,
me a - gain,

it's just the ra - di - o.
and play your sad gui - tar.

Don't you re - mem - ber you told me you loved me ba - by? You

said you'd be com - ing back this way a - gain.

Ba - by, ba - by, ba - by, ba - by,

ba - by,
I love you,
I real - ly do.

I real - ly do.

Only Yesterday

Words by John Bettis. Music by Richard Carpenter.

Yesterday Once More

Words & Music by Richard Carpenter & John Bettis.

Drusilla Penny

Words by John Bettis. Music by Richard Carpenter.

Rainy Days and Mondays

Words by Paul Williams. Music by Roger Nichols.

feel-in' like I don't be-long.___ Walk-in' a-round, some kind of lone-ly clown,

rain-y days and Mon-days al-ways get me down.___

BRIDGE

Fun-ny, but it seems I al-ways wind up here with you,___ nice to know that some-one

loves__ me. Fun-ny, but it seems that it's the on-ly thing to do,___

run and find the one who loves__ me.

Sing

Words & Music by Joe Raposo.

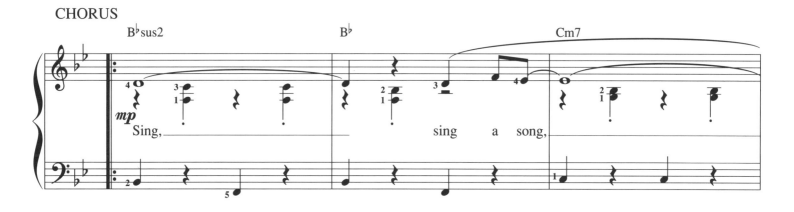

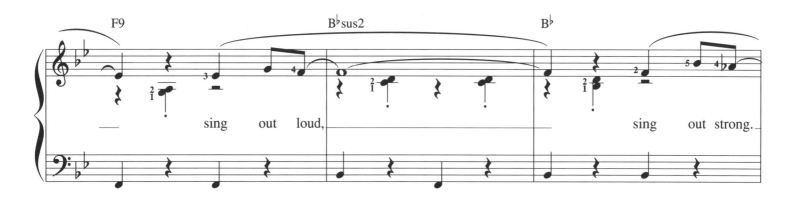

Crystal Lullaby

Words by John Bettis. Music by Richard Carpenter.

Peacefully ♩ = 88

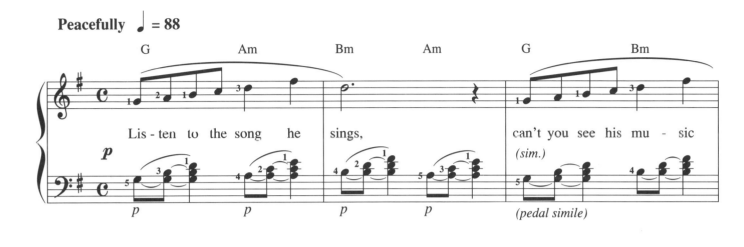

Lis - ten to the song he sings, can't you see his mu - sic

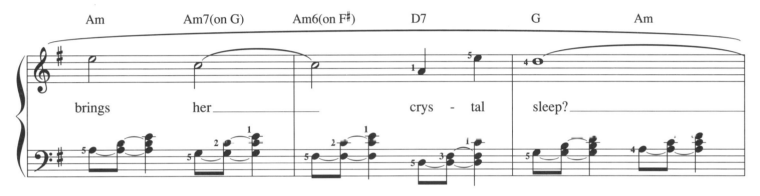

brings her_____ crys - tal sleep?_____

And her hea - vy eye - lids fall, he's

tak - ing her to where the dolls rule the world.

(They Long to Be) Close To You

Words by Hal David. Music by Burt Bacharach.